P9-AZX-534

Miss Mary Mack

A Traditional Chant
Pictures by Evan Polenghi

SCHOLASTIC INC.

New York   Toronto   London   Auckland   Sydney

No part of this publication may be reproduced in whole or in part,
or stored in a retrieval system, or transmitted in any form or by any means,
electronic, mechanical, photocopying, recording, or otherwise, without
written permission of the publisher. For information regarding permission,
write to Scholastic Inc., 555 Broadway, New York, NY 10012.

Copyright © 1994 by Scholastic Inc.
All rights reserved. Published by Scholastic Inc.
Printed in the U.S.A.
ISBN 0-590-27537-2

2 3 4 5 6 7 8 9 10   08   00 99 98 97 96 95 94

Miss Mary Mack, Mack, Mack,
All dressed in black, black, black,

With silver buttons, buttons, buttons,
All down her back, back, back.

She asked her mother, mother, mother,
For 50 cents, cents, cents,

To see the elephant, elephant, elephant,
Jump over the fence, fence, fence.

He jumped so high, high, high,
He reached the sky, sky, sky,

And he never came back, back, back,
Until the Fourth of July.

8